Let's Have Lunch!

Isabel Thomas

Illustrated by Catherine Pape

Schofield & Sims

Lunch is going to be extra fun this week.
It's the week the children all bring in
a dish!

The children all cook food they love.
Then they bring some in for lunch.

Miss Brown peels the tinfoil off the containers.

There is so much food! The children
are going to have some. You can join
them too!

Sasha has an empanada. It looks like a little moon.

Oops! She's spilling the filling on her cardigan!

carrot

mushroom

beef

sweetcorn

Ed has broth. He's picking up squid with chopsticks.

Dim sum are little dumplings with stuffing. They are a good food for picnics.

Erin loves the lentil sambar. But the peppers are as hot as the sun!

Jess has some yogurt to cool them down. That's better!

Now for something sweet! Aiden has carrot and raisin muffins.

He's explaining how to cook them.

You need to add buttermilk to the muffin mix.

Now it is Amal's turn. In her tin there is lots of lokma.

It is crisp and smells of lemons.

Yum! The children all agree the food was so good! They pin the flags from the food on the map.